CHOSEN TO TAKE PART IN A TOP-SECRET GOVERNMENT
PROGRAM, WADE WILSON WAS BESTOWED WITH THE
ABILITY TO HEAL FROM ANY WOUND. HE BECAME A
MERCENARY. THEN, FOR A WHILE, HE TRIED TO BE A HERO.

KELLY THOMPSON
WRITER

DEADPOOL #1-4

CHRIS BACHALO
PENCILER

WAYNE FAUCHER (#1-4),
TIM TOWNSEND (#1-2, #4),
AL VEY (#1-4),
JAIME MENDOZA (#1-4),
LIVESAY (#1-4),
VICTOR OLAZABA (#1-3)
& DEREK FRIDOLFS (#4)
INKERS

DAVID CURIEL
COLOR ARTIST

CHRIS BACHALO & TIM TOWNSEND
COVER ART

"JEFF & WADE"

IRENE STRYCHALSKI
ARTIST

RACHELLE ROSENBERG
COLOR ARTIST

KING DEADPOOL VOL. 1. Contains material originally published in magazine form as DEADPOOL (2019) #1-6. First printing 2020. ISBN 978-1-302-92103-3. Published by MARVEL WORLDWIDE, INC., a subsidiary of MARVEL ENTERTAINMENT, LLC. OFFICE OF PUBLICATION: 1290 Avenue of the Americas, New York, NY 10104. © 2020 MARVEL No similarity between any of the names, characters, persons, and/or institutions in this magazine with those of any living or dead person or institution is intended, and any such similarity which may exist is purely coincidental. Printed in Canada. KEVIN FEIGE, Chief Creative Officer; DAN BUCKLEY, President, Marvel Entertainment; JOHN NEE, Publisher; JOE QUESADA, EVP & Creative Director; TOM BREVOORT, SVP of Publishing; DAVID BOGART, Associate Publisher & SVP of Talent Affairs; Publishing & Partnership; DAVID GABRIEL, VP of Print & Digital Publishing; JEFF YOUNGQUIST, VP of Production & Special Projects; DAN CARR, Executive Director of Publishing Technology; ALEX MORALES, Director of Publishing Operations; DAN EDINGTON, Managing Editor; RICKEY PURDIN, Director of Talent Relations; SUSAN CRESPI, Production Manager; STAN LEE, Chairman Emeritus. For information regarding advertising in Marvel Comics or on Marvel.com, please contact Vit DeBellis, Custom Solutions & Integrated Advertising Manager, at vdebellis@marvel.com. For Marvel subscription inquiries, please call 888-511-5480. Manufactured between 8/19/2020 and 9/15/2020 by SOLISCO PRINTERS, SCOTT, QC, CANADA.

10 9 8 7 6 5 4 3 2 1

It... Well, it went pretty badly. So badly that
Wade decided to go back to being a classic chaos
agent, the Merc with the Mouth, the Regeneratin'
Degenerate known as...

DEADPOOL #5

GERARDO SANDOVAL
PENCILER

VICTOR NAVA
WITH **GERARDO SANDOVAL**
INKERS

CHRIS SOTOMAYOR
COLOR ARTIST

GERARDO SANDOVAL
COVER ART

DEADPOOL #6

KEVIN LIBRANDA
ARTIST

CHRIS SOTOMAYOR
COLOR ARTIST

GREG LAND & JESUS ABURTOV
COVER ART

VC'S JOE SABINO
LETTERER

| SALENA MAHINA | LINDSEY COHICK | JAKE THOMAS |
| LOGO | ASSISTANT EDITOR | EDITOR |

DEADPOOL CREATED BY ROB LIEFELD & FABIAN NICIEZA

COLLECTION EDITOR JENNIFER GRÜNWALD
ASSISTANT MANAGING EDITOR MAIA LOY
ASSISTANT MANAGING EDITOR LISA MONTALBANO
EDITOR, SPECIAL PROJECTS MARK D. BEAZLEY
VP PRODUCTION & SPECIAL PROJECTS JEFF YOUNGQUIST
BOOK DESIGNERS SALENA MAHINA WITH CARLOS LAO
SVP PRINT, SALES & MARKETING DAVID GABRIEL
EDITOR IN CHIEF C.B. CEBULSKI

STATEN ISLAND.

I SO HATE BEING RIGHT.

ARE YOU ALL RIGHT, SIR?

SIR? SIR IS MY DAD, KID. I'M SIR DEADPOOL.

SIR DEADPOOL... ARE YOU ALL RIGHT?

FROM THE FEEL OF IT I'M HALF ALL RIGHT.

YUP. YUP. AS I THOUGHT. YOU KNOW, YOU REALLY NEVER FORGET THE FEELING OF BEING TORN IN HALF. IT'S UNIQUE AMONG INJURIES.

LOOKS DREADFUL. CAN I POSSIBLY ASSIST YOU?

YEAH, HELP ME DRAG THAT OTHER HALF OVER HERE SO I CAN KNIT BACK TOGETHER RATHER THAN REGROW ALL OF IT. IT'LL SAVE TONS OF TIME.

THIS FEELS TERRIBLY INAPPROPRIATE.

WHY HAVE YOU TRIED TO KILL THE KING OF MONSTERS, SIR DEADPOOL?

WHY DO ANY OF US TRY TO KILL A MONSTER KING, SON? FOR MONEY.

LIKE I SAID, LOTS OF PLANS. LIKE A BIG FANCY DINNER WITH ALL MY FRIENDS.

AM I... KIDNAPPED?!

*KID*NAPPED? YOU'RE LIKE FORTY.

YOU WANT SOME OF THIS PIZZA? I ALSO GOT NOODLES.

WE TRADED WITTY BARBS OVER CHIC COCKTAILS. IT WAS A DELIGHT.

THEN THERE WAS THE FANCY ROOF PARTY. SOMEONE BROUGHT A CAKE. THERE WERE THOSE SWANKY PAPER LANTERNS AND A...AN ICE SCULPTURE.

MMF!

WHAT DO YOU MEAN YOU WON'T DELIVER TO ME ANYMORE? I NEED CAKE!

AND OF COURSE THE PRESENTS. MY GOD, THE *PRESENTS*. PEOPLE REALLY OUTDID THEMSELVES.

AND I DEFINITELY DID *NOT* KIDNAP THE MAILMAN JUST SO I'D HAVE SOMEONE TO TALK TO. I DON'T KNOW WHERE YOU HEARD THAT, BUT IT'S NOT A THING.

WILLIE LUMPKIN WOULD HAVE BEEN WAY COOLER ABOUT THIS, KARL.

SLURRRRP

BUT YOU KNOW, I GOT TO THINKING ABOUT THIS CLIENT... MAYBE HE REALLY NEEDED HELP.

I LEFT MY FRIENDS ON THE ROOF, EATING MY CAKE, AND I TOOK THE FERRY OUT TO STATEN ISLAND.

SO MY CONSCIENCE GOT THE BETTER OF ME.

PRETTY HEROIC, RIGHT?

SEEMED LIKE SOMETHING WEIRD WAS GOING ON BUT, Y'KNOW, NOT MY PROBLEM. OR IT WASN'T BACK THEN.

IN THE GOOD OL' DAYS.

YOU BLAYLOCK?

DEADPOOL.

NO, THAT'S ME. *I'M* DEADPOOL.

CHARMING.

THE JOB IS SIMPLE, MR. POOL... YOU KILL THIS NEWFANGLED *"KING OF MONSTERS"* THAT HAS SPEARHEADED THE MONSTERS' CLAIM TO STATEN ISLAND AND THIS MASS *IMMIGRATION.*

NOT THAT I DON'T WANT YOUR MONEY, BUT WHY NOT JUST WAIT FOR SOME HERO TYPES TO COME BY AND CLEAN THIS UP FOR YOU?

I MEAN, IT'S *STATEN ISLAND,* SO IT'LL TAKE THEM A MINUTE TO CARE, BUT THEY'LL GET HERE EVENTUALLY.

UNFORTUNATELY, IT SEEMS THE MONSTERS' CLAIM IS LEGAL. SOME SEVENTEENTH-CENTURY DEAL WITH DESPERATE HUMANS.

THE COURTS ARE FIGHTING. BUT WE CAN ILL AFFORD TO WAIT THAT OUT... IT COULD TAKE DECADES.

MEANWHILE, EVERY DAY MORE MONSTERS STREAM IN FROM MONSTEROPOLIS, MONSTER ISLAND...AND GOD KNOWS WHERE ELSE.

BUT THIS *"MONSTER KING"* OF THEIRS SEEMS TO BE THE MASTERMIND. WE BELIEVE WITHOUT HIM TO LEAD THEM, THE REST WILL GIVE UP AND GO HOME.

YEAH, YOU KNOW WHAT? I'M GONNA PASS. I DON'T REALLY HAVE A PROBLEM WITH MONSTERS, AND ARE--

--N'T MONSTERS *THE WORST?* I'M ON THE CASE!

CLIK

YOU GET THE REST WHEN THE JOB IS DONE.

THAP

DON'T TRY TO STIFF ME, BLAYLOCK.

THAT DOESN'T GO WELL FOR PEOPLE!

JUST DO AS YOU WERE HIRED AND YOU'LL GET ALL THAT YOU'RE OWED AND MORE.

OOOH. A BONUS. I LOVE A BONUS.

SO THIS MONSTER KING... I'M GUESSING HE'S A BIG GUY?

BLAYLOCK?

AND *THAT*, YOUNG MONSTER--

BELLUS.

--YOUNG MONSTER BELLUS, IS HOW I CAME TO BE HERE.

AND AS SOON AS MY SPINE FINISHES KNITTING ITSELF BACK TOGETHER I'M GOING TO SHOVE LIKE FORTY GRENADES DOWN THAT MONSTER KING'S THROAT.

UM...

WHAT?

WELL, I AM LORD CHAMBERLAIN TO THE CURRENT MONSTER KING... SO...

WHAT HAPPENED TO BELLUS?

BELLUS IS MY NAME. LORD CHAMBERLAIN IS MY POSITION.

?

I AM A MONSTER BORN INTO ROYAL SERVICE. I CAN TRANSLATE HUNDREDS OF--

THINGS DON'T USUALLY GO WELL FOR THAT GUY, BELLUS.

NO, THEY DON'T, SIR.

WELL, ARE YOU GONN GET IN MY WAY TO SA YOUR KING, KID?

...NO, SIR. I DO NOT *LIKE* OUR NEW KING. AND I DO NOT LIKE THIS *STATEN ISLAND*. THE PEOPLE DO NOT WANT US HERE.

I GOT NEWS FOR YOU, KID CHAMBERLAIN... YOU CAN'T LISTEN TO WHAT OTHER PEOPLE WANT.

PEOPLE ARE TERRIBLE AND THEY'RE AFRAID OF WHAT THEY DON'T UNDERSTAND.

%$&#. I... I THINK I JUST QUOTED THE X-MEN'S FAMILY CREST. NEVER GONNA LIVE *THAT*--

KRNNCH

HRRRRK!

KCK--YOU--KKK--MIND TAKING YOUR BOOT OFF MY--KKK--NECK?

I--HRKKK--I JUST HEALED THAT BIT.

ARE YOU GOING TO KILL HER, SIR?

WE'LL SEE. DAY'S STILL YOUNG!

ELSA, WHAT ARE YOU DOING HERE?

HMMPH, SO SAY WE ALL.

I'M HERE FOR THE MONSTER KING.

WELL, HE'S BLOODY BIG, ISN'T HE?

MAYBE THIS'LL BE ONE OF THOSE DAVID AND GOLIATH TYPE OF THINGS.

DIDN'T HE ALREADY RIP YOU IN HALF ONCE TODAY?

I MEAN, I DIDN'T SAY IT WAS A *PERFECT* DAVID AND GOLIATH THING.

JUST STAY OUT OF MY ⊗⊗⊗⊗ WAY, WADE.

IMPOSSIBLE BECAUSE OF HOW MUCH YOU'LL BE STAYING OUT OF *MY* WAY!

AHHHHH!

NOOO!

GRÄH.

KA-THOOM

FREEEEEEE!

BLAM BLAM

BLAM

RRRRRRRAWWWWRRR

HE HAS TERRIBLE BREATH, AM I RIGHT?

DIDN'T LIKE THAT, NOW, DID HE?

DON'T SUPPOSE YOU TRIED TALKING TO HIM?

I DID, ACTUALLY! WHEN WE FIRST MET EARLY THIS MORNING.

"DIDN'T GO GREAT."

SO MUCH FOR DIPLOMACY.

I HAVE TO SAY, HIS FLESH IS VERY EASY TO PIERCE. HE'S VULNERABLE... THIS SHOULDN'T TAKE TERRIBLY LONG.

BLAM

BLAM

DON'T &$%# JINX US, BLOODSTONE!

FIVE SECONDS LATER.

WHAT DID I SAY?!

Y'KNOW, I WAS IN A SITUATION LIKE THIS ONCE BEFORE WITH SPIDER-MAN, BUT THIS IS BETTER, YOU SEEM MUCH LESS UPTIGHT.

LIKE, FOR A GUY WHO DRESSES IN SKINTIGHT SPANDEX AND SHOOTS ALL OVER THE CITY WHAT ONE CAN ONLY DESCRIBE AS A VERY THINLY VEILED METAPHOR FOR A VERY PRIVATE ACT, YOU'D THINK HE'D BE LESS CONSERVATIVE, BUT--

WADE. IF YOU DON'T SHUT UP, I'M GOING TO THINK YOU DON'T BLOODY KNOW WHAT A MOUTH IS FOR.

WHOA. *THAT* IS DEFINITELY NOT AGE-APPROPRIATE, AND I LOVE IT!

WAIT. NO! TAKE ME! I WON'T STAND FOR THIS INSULT! I'M FAR MORE DELICIOUS! I'M FULL OF CANCER-- SHE'S JUST SILICONE!

CHOP CHOP CHOPPITY CHOP CHOP

SHE. CAN'T. HAVE. MY. GOLD. BARS.

SLICE!

DICE!

JULIENNE FRIES!

I GOT YOU, GIRL.

YEAH, BUT WHO'S GOT YOU?

ONE THING AT A TIME!

CHOMP

YOUR ARM!

THAK

WADE! YOU LOST YOUR WHOLE SODDING ARM!

ALL PART OF THE PLAN. I MEAN, I TOLD HIM I WAS GOING TO KILL HIM WITH FORTY GRENADES... WHY DOES NOBODY TAKE ME SERIOUSLY, ELSA?

?

RWARRGH!

Y'SEE, THAT ARM HAD ALL THE GRENADES...

...BUT I KEEP THE **PINS** IN MY OTHER ARM. SHHHHH!

!@!&!@&!*

STAY DOWN, WADE!

HRRRRK.

AS YOU SHIELD ME FROM FLAMING MONSTER CHUNKS, IT OCCURS TO ME THAT MAYBE YOU LIKE ME.

IT OCCURS TO **ME** THAT YOU'RE SUFFERING FROM HEAD TRAUMA.

SO YOU RUB YOUR SEXY PARTS UP AGAINST JUST ANYONE?

DON'T FLATTER YOURSELF. I'D RATHER RUB UP AGAINST THE FLAMING MONSTER CHUNKS...

BUT YOU SAVED ME. THAT EARNS YOU **AT LEAST** A HUMAN SHIELD.

AND YET... YOU'RE NOT MOVING.

JUST SO WE'RE CLEAR, THERE'S NOTHING SILICONE ABOUT ME, DARLING.

SEE. AGAIN. THIS BEHAVIOR MAKES IT SEEM LIKE YOU LIKE ME.

NOPE.

<...SO MY NEW NEIGHBOR INGESTED THREE OF MY UNBORNS FOR HIS SUNDAY BREAKFAST SCRAMBLE AND I ONLY ATE *ONE* OF HIS FURRY CHILDREN IN RETRIBUTION, AND YOU SHOULD HEAR THE FUSS HE'S MAKING!>*

<UNBELIEVABLE.>**

<SO I COME ALL THE WAY OUT HERE TO ASK FOR A MEDAL COMMENDING MY RESTRAINT AND GOOD CITIZENRY TO SHOVE IN MY NEIGHBOR'S FACE AND NOW I'M LIKE, *"WHO IS THIS NEW GUY?"*>

<I KNOW, RIGHT?>

*TRANSLATED FROM... WEIRD BIRD-MONSTERESE? --ED.

**TRANSLATED FROM COMMON ZOMBIE VERNACULAR. --ED.

NEXT, THIS GENTLEMAN IS REQUESTING A MEDAL OF GOOD CITIZENRY FOR... WHAT WAS YOUR STORY AGAIN, SIR?

OH, MY. THAT IS QUITE THE TALE!

SQUUUAAWK!

≈SIGH≈ I WONDER IF I CAN TRICK ONE OF THESE IDIOTS INTO KILLING ME AND SETTING ME FREE.

WAIT. WHO ARE THOSE GUYS? THEY DON'T LOOK LIKE THE REGULAR SCHLUBS I'VE BEEN LISTENING TO SO FAR.

HE DIDN'T PISS OFF ANYONE. HE JUST UNDERSTANDS *DUTY.*

OH, AND *I* DON'T? THAT'S THE IMPLICATION THERE? YEAH, REAL SUBTLE. I DIDN'T CATCH *YOUR* NAME IN ALL THOSE NAMES.

I AM LE LOUP QUI PÉTRIFIE, THE WOLF THAT PETRIFIES, FIRST OF MY NAME. MYTHICAL WOLF GOD LA BÊTE QUI MARCHE. BEDEVILED A HUNDRED YEARS AGO BY THE BITE OF A HUMAN, I WAS REMADE AS *THE NIGHT WOLF,* CURSED TO WALK THE EARTH--

ALL RIGHT ALREADY, GAME OF THRONES. YOU'RE A VERY FANCY WOLF GUY. WE GET IT. THAT'S A LOT OF NAMES, SO I'M JUST GONNA CALL YOU CHAD, OKAY?

NO. IT IS NOT *"OKAY."*

WHATEVER, *CHAD.*

AHEM. HIGHNESS, A LITTLE RESPECT IF YOU DON'T MIND... THESE WERE THE PREVIOUS KINGS' HONOR GUARD, HIS PROTECTORS...

HUH. WELL, NOT SO GREAT AT YOUR JOB, ARE YOU?

HOW DARE--

LISTEN, I KILLED YOUR KING AND I DIDN'T EVEN *SEE* YOU JOKERS...SO IT SEEMS LIKE YOU GUYS &@%# BLOW.

SIRE, THE PREVIOUS KING HAD SENT THEM AWAY ON A MISSION. THEY'VE ONLY JUST RETURNED NOW.

OH, I SEE. AND YOU'RE FEELING GUILTY.

...

YEAH. FAIR ENOUGH.

YEAH, I HEAR YOU AND I **DON'T CARE.** YOU CAN'T KEEP HARASSING THE FERRIES. YOU DO THAT AND THEN CAPTAIN AMERICA SHOWS UP AND THAT'S A WHOLE HEADACHE FOR ME.

I DON'T CARE FOR LOOKING LIKE AN IDIOT IN FRONT OF CAP. IT HAPPENS ALL THE TIME, BUT I **DO. NOT. CARE. FOR. IT.**

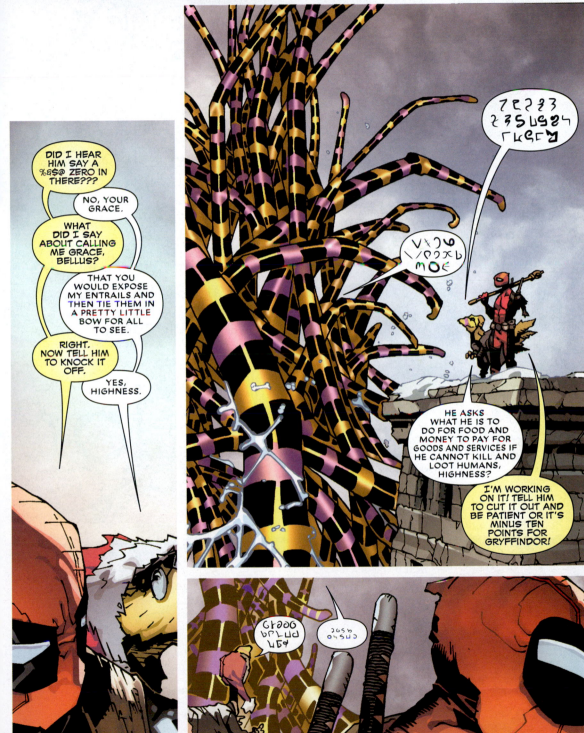

DID I HEAR HIM SAY A %&$@ ZERO IN THERE???

NO, YOUR GRACE.

WHAT DID I SAY ABOUT CALLING ME GRACE, BELLUS?

THAT YOU WOULD EXPOSE MY ENTRAILS AND THEN TIE THEM IN A PRETTY LITTLE BOW FOR ALL TO SEE.

RIGHT. NOW TELL HIM TO KNOCK IT OFF.

YES, HIGHNESS.

HE ASKS WHAT HE IS TO DO FOR FOOD AND MONEY TO PAY FOR GOODS AND SERVICES IF HE CANNOT KILL AND LOOT HUMANS, HIGHNESS?

I'M WORKING ON IT! TELL HIM TO CUT IT OUT AND BE PATIENT OR IT'S MINUS TEN POINTS FOR GRYFFINDOR!

WHAT THE...

...WHO'S THIS?

GRRRRRRR.

KRRNCH

THAT'S JEFF. HE'S A LAND SHARK.

OH, HEY GWEN.

GWENPOOL. LESS LIKE A DEADPOOL THAN YOU MIGHT THINK, BUT ALSO MORE LIKE A DEADPOOL THAN YOU MIGHT THINK? KID'S GOT SPUNK. I LIKE HER.

YEAH, I'VE GOT EYES, CUTE.

YOU TRYING TO DROP HIM OFF FOR MONSTER DAY CARE OR WHAT? 'CUZ WE DON'T DO THAT...YET.

GRRRRRRRRRRRR!

I...*SNIFF*

WAIT. WHAT DID I DO? PLEASE DON'T %@&# CRY. THAT'S THE LAST THING I CAN TAKE RIGHT NOW.

I...YOU GOTTA TAKE HIM FOR ME, WADE.

WHAT? NO. WHAT? WHY? WHY WOULD I DO THAT?

I...HE... HE'S A SHARK. HE'LL BE SAFER HERE.

GWEN! DOES ANYTHING ABOUT THIS PLACE LOOK &$#@ SAFE?!

IT IS NOT, MA'AM.

GRRRRRRR.

IT'S...IT'S NOT JUST THAT. I...I KEEP LOSING MY BOOKS. IN ORDER TO SURVIVE HE NEEDS A RELIABLE BOOK... YOU *ALWAYS* HAVE A BOOK.

HE'LL SURVIVE IF I LEAVE HIM IN YOUR NARRATIVE... I DON'T KNOW WHAT HAPPENS TO HIM IF HE STAYS IN MINE.

WHAT DO YOU MEAN IT'S NOT FREE? I'M A KING.

UH... KING OF WHAT?

THE MONSTERS! AND THUS ALSO STATEN ISLAND! READ A NEWSPAPER, KID!

WHAT'S A NEWSPAPER?

JUST GIVE ME THE KING DISCOUNT!

I--UH... THERE'S NO BUTTON FOR THAT, SIR. I CAN GIVE YOU THE...UH...SENIOR DISCOUNT? MAYBE?

UGH! FINE!

ALSO, WE DON'T HAVE ANY "MEATY" FLAVORS... I, UM...DON'T EVEN KNOW WHAT THAT MEANS.

THEY DON'T HAVE ANY MEAT ICE CREAM, JEFF. WHAT ABOUT...CHUNKY NOT-MONKEY...THAT SOUNDS MEATY-ISH.

GRRRRRRRR.

SOLD. TWO OF YOUR BIGGEST CHUNKY NOT-MONKEYS.

LATER.
HOME OF LORD CHAMBERLAIN BELLUS, STATEN ISLAND.

OH DEAR. POWER OUTAGE. WE'LL HAVE TO ADD THAT TO THE TO-DO LIST.

I HOPE IT'S NOT THOSE PESKY NYFLOCKS AGAIN.

IT'S
NOT.

GRACIOUS!

SHHUNNNNK

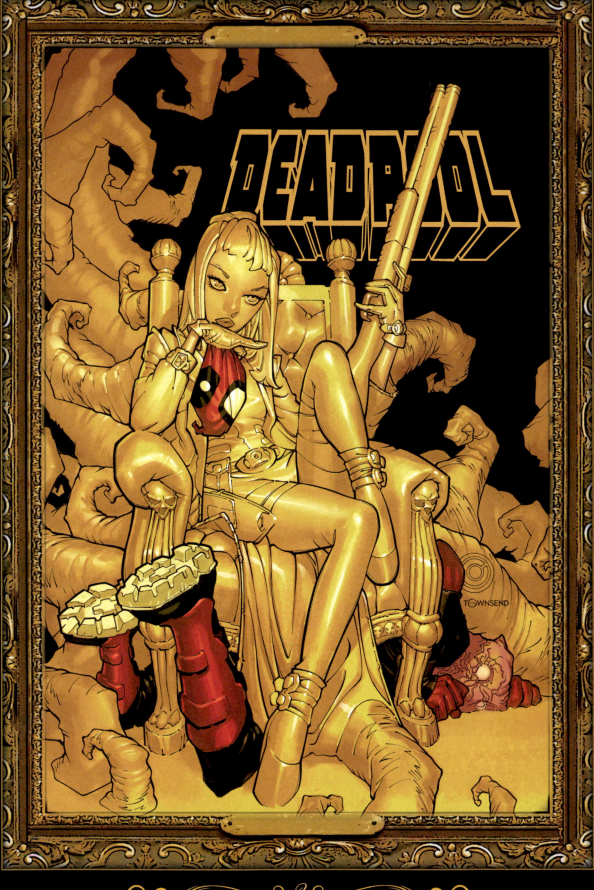

THIS CRAP IS CRAZY, RIGHT?

I MEAN, NOT ME AS A KING. TO BE HONEST, THAT'S *WAY* OVERDUE.

LIKE, I SHOULD HAVE BEEN MADE A KING OF SOMETHING A LONG DAMN TIME AGO... KING OF JOKES, KING OF MERCS, KING OF GREAT PICK-UP LINES, KING OF WEAPONS, KING OF GOOD IDEAS...

ALL RIGHT, FINE, THAT LAST ONE'S A STRETCH.

UH, SNOWGUY? WHATCHU DOIN' WITH JEFF?

MRRRR?

YUM.

HEY, MAN, DON'T... DON'T DO THAT.

MRRRRR?

HOLD ON. THIS STUPID SNOWMAN HAS EATEN MY BEST FRIEND.

YOU DO THIS AGAIN AND IT'S GONNA BE A TELEPORTATION RIGHT INTO THE BOWELS OF THE SUN, YOU GET ME, SNOWMAN?

YANK YANK

SORRY. I'VE GOTTEN OFF TRACK. WHAT I'M TRYING TO SAY IS THIS ISN'T ABOUT ME. WELL, YEAH, IT IS. I MEAN, I'M THE *STAR*. BUT IT'S NOT *JUST* ABOUT ME. NOT ANYMORE.

MMMMRRR!

THIS IS ABOUT SO MUCH MORE NOW. THIS IS ABOUT *ALL* OF US.

MONSTERS AND HUMANS LIVING IN PEACE...MOSTLY. RESIDENTS AND VISITORS ALIKE CAN ENJOY OUR INNOVATIVE GREEN INITIATIVES, LIKE A MONSTER THAT EATS ALL OUR GARBAGE--

--AND BETTER YET, FART MONSTERS THAT ABSORB THE GAS PRODUCED BY SAID GARBAGE MONSTER-- A NEARLY PERFECT SYSTEM!

TRULY A MARVEL!

PROGRESSIVE INITIATIVES LIKE THIS MAKE OUR NEW ISLAND A PERFECT PLACE TO LIVE, WORK, AND PLAY!

NOM NOM NOM

POOT

MMM. YUM.

FOR EXAMPLE, TAKE A RIDE ON OUR NEW MONSTER FERRY. CHEAPER, FASTER, AND GREENER THAN THE ORIGINAL FERRIES, BUT ALSO WAY MORE FUN.

HI, MOM!

IT IS ADMITTEDLY SLIIIIIGHTLY MORE DANGEROUS, BUT WHO WANTS TO LIVE FOREVER?! TAKE A RISK!

AND IT'S STILL SAFER THAN CAR TRAVEL, KIDS!

THAT'S RIGHT, *PLAY*--WE'RE NOT *JUST* ABOUT BORING ENVIRONMENTAL ADVANCES!

I STILL THINK HE SHOULD DO A TAKE WITHOUT THE MASK. IT'S HARD TO TRUST SOMEONE WITH A MASK ON.

HAVE YOU SEEN WHAT'S UNDER THERE? IT'S *MESSED* UP. IT'S LIKE UNCOOKED HAMBURGER.

SO WHAT?

I MEAN...HE'S A *MONSTER.*

OH YEAH? THAT'S WHAT YOU THINK, *HUH?*

UH.

SORRY.

÷GULP÷

I HATE IT!

REALLY? I LOVE IT!

HUH?

YIKES!

SPLACK

ANNNNND THE KRAKEN ATE A BOAT. ON FILM. GREAT.

SIGH.

HIGHNESS? UM...I DON'T WANT TO BE TOO RIGID HERE, BUT A "SIGH" AND A "SHOULDER SLUMP" ARE DEFINITELY NOT IN THE SCRIPT.

WE GOTTA TAKE TEN...NO, TWENTY. A SOFT TWENTY.

AND MAKE SURE NOTHING ELSE EATS ANYTHING ELSE WHILE I'M GONE! OR, IF IT DOES, FOR GOD'S SAKE DON'T FILM IT!

KING DEADPOOL'S ROUNDISH TABLE.

CHET MORITA.

QUONIAN.

KOHLAAB THE PILE.

BÜN-BÜN THE DESTROYER.

THE NIGHT WOLF.

ZRRGO, SON OF ORRGO THE UNCONQUERABLE.

WHY HAVEN'T YOU GUYS FOUND BELLUS YET?!

WE THINK HE MIGHT HAVE HAD A HOUSE OUTSIDE OF THE QUARTERS HE HAD HERE. WE'RE SEARCHING EVERYWHERE.

JEFF!

LISTEN, WE HAVE TO DIG DEEP. I WANT HIM FOUND. NOT ONLY IS IT EMBARRASSING AS HELL TO LOSE MY RIGHT-HAND MAN ON DAY ONE, BUT...I REALLY LIKED THAT KID--

--UNLESS... WAITAMINUTE!

DID BELLUS BETRAY ME?! LIKE HE DID THE LAST KING?! MY GOD, WAS I TAKEN IN BY HIS INSANE CUTENESS?! WHAT A FOOL I AM!

MUCH AS I TEND TO AGREE WITH THAT LAST BIT, HIGHNESS, IF YOU COULD DO ME A FAVOR AND NOT SPIN OUT RIGHT NOW I'D APPRECIATE IT. I'M AFRAID WE HAVE A MUCH BIGGER PROBLEM THAN BELLUS.

NO. NO MORE PROBLEMS. I AM MAXED OUT ON PROBLEMS.

BELLUS ISN'T THE ONLY ONE MISSING, HIGHNESS. WE'VE GOTTEN REPORTS OF A DOZEN CITIZENS-- ALL MONSTERS--THAT HAVE DISAPPEARED OVER THE LAST WEEK.

YOU HAVE GOT TO BE KIDDING ME.

WHEN WILL THIS JOB BE FUN? WHEN?!

ALL RIGHT. I'M FINISHING THIS COMMERCIAL AND THEN WE'RE DEALING WITH THIS. YOU GUYS, COME WITH ME.

WE'RE A LITTLE BUSY HERE.

NOT GETTING MUCH DONE THOUGH, ARE YOU? I NEED MONSTERS THAT I CAN CONTROL TO FINISH THIS COMMERCIAL.

THE OTHER ONES KEEP EATING THINGS WHILE WE'RE FILMING. I'M SPENDING A FORTUNE IN FILM STOCK...AMONG OTHER THINGS.

WE'RE SOLDIERS, NOT PERFORMERS... AND WE'RE NOT YOUR PUPPETS.

UM, I'M THE KING OF YOU. YOU'RE PUPPETS IF I SAY YOU'RE PUPPETS.

AND YOU, BUN-BUN, YOU'RE ADORABLE. WE'LL PUT YOU RIGHT UP FRONT.

YIKES! ON SECOND THOUGHT...MAYBE IN THE BACK FOR YOU.

COME NOW, MY DEADLY PUPPETS! LET US MAKE MAGIC AND FUTURE TOURISM DOLLARS!

YOU'VE GOT TO BE KIDDING ME.

I DON'T LIKE YOU ENOUGH TO MAKE A ✗✗✗✗ JOKE.

KLIK

SO WHOEVER KILLS THE KING BECOMES THE *NEW* KING?!

WHAT YOU'RE TELLING ME IS THAT I'VE NOW ACCIDENTALLY MADE THE NEW KING OF THE MONSTERS...AND THUS THE RULER OF STATEN ISLAND... *DEADPOOL*.

A SORT-OF HUMAN WHO IS BASICALLY INSANE, PROBABLY CAN'T BE KILLED, AND HAS THE MORAL FIBER OF A MARSHMALLOW.

THIS IS ALL *YOUR* FAULT! IF YOU'D JUST TAKEN THE JOB IN THE FIRST PLACE, I NEVER WOULD HAVE GONE TO HIM! ARE YOU GOING TO FIX THIS?!

I BLOODY WELL TOLD YOU I'D TAKE CARE OF IT, BLAYLOCK, AND I BLOODY WELL WILL.

I HOPE YOU'RE BRINGING MORE THAN THAT RIFLE, BLOODSTONE. DEADPOOL MAYBE CAN'T BE KILLED AT ALL, SO HE CERTAINLY CAN'T BE KILLED BY SOMETHING AS ORDINARY AS A RIFLE.

YOU'RE AN ABSOLUTE MORON, BLAYLOCK. DO I SEEM LIKE A WOMAN WHO CARRIES AROUND AN ORDINARY ✗✗✗✗✗ RIFLE?

KLAK

THAT'S RIGHT, FOLKS. ALL THIS AND MORE CAN BE YOURS. AND FOR A LIMITED TIME, EVERYTHING IS TWENTY PERCENT OFF!

BY GRABTHAR'S HAMMER...WHAT A SAVINGS.

WHAT A SAVINGS INDEED!

AND DON'T FORGET TO VOTE FOR OUR NEW ISLAND NAME AT WWW.KINGPOOL.LOVE!

I DON'T WANNA INFLUENCE ANYONE, BUT SO FAR THE LEADING CONTENDER IS ISLANDY MCISLANDFACE, SO, Y'KNOW, HELP US MAKE...BETTER CHOICES.

ISLANDY MCISLANDFACE, WADE? REALLY?

PLEASEDON'TLET THATBECAPPLEASE DON'TLETTHATBECAP PLEASEDON'TLET THATBE--

DAMMIT!

A WORD, WADE?

UM, IF YOU HAVEN'T NOTICED, CAP, KINDA IN THE MIDDLE OF SOMETHING HERE?

IT'S IMPORTANT, WADE.

ALL RIGHT. SURE. WE CAN TAKE FIVE FOR CAPTAIN AMERICA.

THE UPCOMING SUNRISE WON'T KILL HALF OUR CREW OR ANYTHING.

LET'S JUST TAKE A LITTLE WALK. I CAN SHOW YOU AROUND, YOU CAN YELL AT ME--IT'LL BE LIKE OLD TIMES. AMAZING.

MR. STEVE, IF I COULD DIRECT YOUR ATTENTION OVER HERE--

KEEP FILMING!

--YOU'LL NOTICE OUR INNOVATIVE FART MONSTERS.

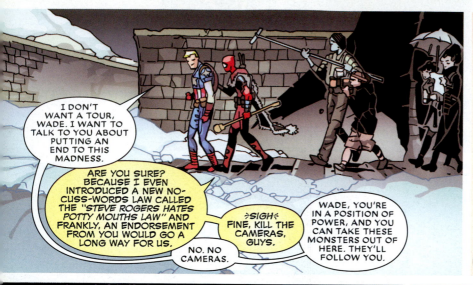

I DON'T WANT A TOUR, WADE. I WANT TO TALK TO YOU ABOUT PUTTING AN END TO THIS MADNESS.

ARE YOU SURE? BECAUSE I EVEN INTRODUCED A NEW NO-CUSS-WORDS LAW CALLED THE "STEVE ROGERS HATES POTTY MOUTHS LAW" AND FRANKLY, AN ENDORSEMENT FROM YOU WOULD GO A LONG WAY FOR US.

≷SIGH≷ FINE, KILL THE CAMERAS, GUYS.

NO. NO CAMERAS.

WADE, YOU'RE IN A POSITION OF POWER, AND YOU CAN TAKE THESE MONSTERS OUT OF HERE. THEY'LL FOLLOW YOU.

THIS IS A POWDER KEG OF A SITUATION, AND WHEN IT GOES BAD A LOT OF INNOCENT PEOPLE ARE GOING TO GET KILLED.

YOU MEAN PEOPLE AND MONSTERS, RIGHT, CAP?

YOU MEANT TO SAY INNOCENT PEOPLE AND INNOCENT MONSTERS, RIGHT?

WHAT?

...OF COURSE.

LISTEN, I GET IT--YOU'RE A HERO, BUT AT THE END OF THE DAY YOU'RE ALSO HUMAN...SO FOR YOU--PEOPLE THAT LOOK LIKE YOU, THEY COME FIRST.

THAT'S NOT--

BUT WE'RE NOT ALL YOU, STEVE...

...YOU REMEMBER WHAT I AM, RIGHT?

DON'T DO THAT, WADE. DON'T PUT US ON OPPOSITE SIDES OF SOMETHING. WE CAN WORK THIS OUT TOGETHER.

NAH, MAN. IT'S TOO LATE FOR THAT. YOU ALREADY SHOWED YOUR CARDS. I SEE WHERE YOU STAND.

BUT Y'KNOW HOW I ADMIRE YOU, CAP. I'VE EVEN GOT YOUR LIMITED-EDITION COIN SET...THE GOLD PREMIUM "AMERICA'S ASS" ONES.

THEY ARE *CHOICE*. I'VE GOTTEN A LOT OF ENJOYMENT OUT OF THEM, SO I DON'T WANT ANY HARD FEELINGS HERE. LEMME GET YOU A LIFT BACK TO THE CITY. WE'VE GOT THIS TELEPORTER...

THAT'S NOT NECESSARY.

DON'T BE SILLY. HAPPY TO DO IT.

WE CALL HIM *HURL*.

'COURSE THE PROCESS IS ALSO GROSS AS HELL, SO YOU'LL WANNA HURL WHEN YOU GET HOME TOO. IT'S NICE HOW THAT WORKS OUT, ISN'T IT?

BLARRRGGGHHHH

DON'T FORGET TO WRITE, STEVE!

FWASH

OH MY GOD.

WHAT? C'MON. IT WASN'T THAT BAD. STEVE'S GOT A BETTER SENSE OF HUMOR THAN PEOPLE THINK...

IT'S NOT THAT... LOOK.

NO.

I THOUGHT KRAVEN WAS KILLED.

HE WAS. THIS IS THE NEW GUY. SON OF KRAVEN OR WHATEVER. APPARENTLY THINKS HE'S GOING TO MAKE A NAME FOR HIMSELF ON *OUR* ISLAND.

THAT'S NOT GOING TO HAPPEN.

NO, IT IS *NOT*.

GRRRRR.

BOLD WORDS CONSIDERING I HAVE ALREADY KILLED A DOZEN OF YOUR PEOPLE.

BUT IT WAS ALL TOO EASY. SO NOW I AM HERE FOR *YOU*, DEADPOOL.

THAK

SLUMP

OOOOF.

HOO BOY! THAT IS THE GOOD STUFF. MEDICAL-GRADE TRANQUILIZER RIGHT THERE. NOBODY LET THAT CRAP HIT CHET...IT MIGHT KILL HIM.

BUN-BUN'S DOWN. KOHLAAB TOO...NO...WAIT... YES! RALLY, KOHLAAB!

KOHLAAB!

KOHLAAB!

KOHLAAB!

KOHLAAB!

JUST GREAT, IS THAT...IS THAT THE WHOLE TEAM EXCEPT JEFF AND PARTS OF KOHLAAB IN THAT THING?!

C'MON! EIGHT AGAINST ONE, AND WE'RE ALREADY LOSING?! I MEAN, SURE, ONE OF US IS JUST A GUY NAMED CHET, BUT STILL!

KOHLAAB, I'LL COVER YOU. GET UP THERE AND CUT THEM DOWN... ALSO, YOU SHOULD REALLY CONSIDER HAVING A FACE. I MEAN, THIS WAY EVERYWHERE IS JUST BUTTS. AND IT'S AWKWARD. TRULY, DEEPLY AWKWARD.

GROWL GROWL

OH WAIT. NEVER MIND. LOOKS LIKE THEY GOT IT. OR WAIT. NO. IT'S JUST A LOT OF GROWLING MAYBE?

GRRRRRRRR STAY BACK RRRRRR!

I DON'T KNOW HOW ALL THAT GROWLING HELPS, BUT--

SNAP

CRAP.

THUMP

LIKE EVERYTHING IN MY LIFE... THAT COULD HAVE GONE BETTER.

NO.

GRRRRRR.

SWSSH

NOT JEFF!!!

THUNK

GONNA *KOFF* TAKE MORE THAN THAT KNIFE, BOOTLEG MILLENNIAL KRAVEN.

WE WILL SEE.

SORRY IT'S COME TO THIS, BUT I'M AFRAID I'M OUT OF BLOODY OPTIONS.

BOOM

SO MESSY.

THAK

FWASH

WE'RE SUPPOSED TO BELIEVE YOU CARE?

EH. IT'S WHAT YOU'RE SUPPOSED TO SAY.

UH. NO. I DIDN'T. BUT EVEN IF I DID, WHAT ARE YOU GONNA DO ABOUT IT?

BY YOUR OWN DODGY RULES, IF I DID KILL HIM, I'D BE YOUR BLOODY KING NOW.

OH, SOD OFF WITH YOUR THREATS. THIS WHOLE THING WAS GOING PEAR-SHAPED.

AND I DIDN'T EVEN KILL HIM, I SAVED HIM. IN FACT...

00:02

...HE SHOULD BE COMING BACK RIGHT ABOUT...

THDOOMP

WHAT **WAS** THAT?!

NO, I DON'T EVEN CARE!

WHO **DID** THAT?! I'M GONNA KILL THEM.

NO, NO, THAT'S TOO QUICK. SOMETHING SLOWER, LONGER, **MUCH** MORE PAINFUL!

I DID IT, WADE. I SAVED YOUR RUBBISH LIFE. **YOU'RE WELCOME.**

YOU SAVED ME FROM WHAT?! A BIG **KNIFE?!**

I AM **DEADPOOL!!!** I AM NOT AFRAID OF KNIVES!

WHAT I AM NOW AFRAID OF IS WHATEVER TAR-FILLED FORMLESS HELL DIMENSION YOU JUST SENT ME TO WHERE TIME AND SPACE HAD NO MEANING!

IT'S NEW TECH I'M TRYING OUT. EXPERIMENTAL. BY INFUSING THE BULLETS WITH THE BLOOD OF A BONEBEAST MONSTER I WAS ABLE TO HARNESS THEIR TELEPORTING POWER...A.K.A. TELEPORTING BULLETS. PRETTY ✕✕✕✕ COOL, RIGHT?

PRETTY COOL? **PRETTY COOL?!**

NO. NOT COOL, ELSA!

AND JUST WHERE THE HELL IS KRAVEN?!

WE LOST HIM.

&#$%!!!

IS EVERYONE MOBILE? CONSCIOUS?

CHET'S STILL OUT. BUN-BUN CAN CARRY HIM.

WATCH OUT!

ZZZT

HE'S BACK. HONOR GUARD, FORM ON ME.

SIRE. STAY DOWN.

OOF!

ZZZZZZKRKK

PPZZT

LISTEN, YOU'RE VERY HANDSOME, BUT WE BARELY KNOW EACH OTHER...

HILARIOUS.

WHO'S JOKING?

FWIP FWIP FWIP

THUNK THUNK THUNK

THUNK

THAP

UM...THANKS, QUONIAN. YOU UH...YOU OKAY THERE?

QUONIAN IS A BIG TALKER, HUH?

HE'S MUTE. UNDERSTANDS EVERYTHING BUT CANNOT SPEAK.

I GUESS I TALK ENOUGH FOR THE BOTH OF US.

YOU TALK ENOUGH FOR AN ENTIRE VILLAGE.

VILLAGE? WHAT ARE YOU, 200 YEARS OLD?

YES.

ALL RIGHT. WE'VE LITERALLY BEEN LED INTO HIS KILL ZONE. RUNNING IS OUR ONLY OPTION.

THERE'S NO HONOR IN RUNNING. WE. DO. NOT. RUN.

WHAT ABOUT ME SCREAMS "HONOR" TO YOU, WOLF?

WE WANT TO SURVIVE, THEN WE LISTEN TO ME. I'M THE KING OF SURVIVING.

THAT'S NOT--

EVEN IF YOU DISAGREE WITH ME...CONSIDER THIS AN ORDER. FROM YOUR KING.

BUT NOT YOU, BLOODSTONE. YOU'RE ON YOUR OWN. GET THE HELL OFF MY ISLAND BEFORE MY PEOPLE KILL YOU.

AND STOP COMING BACK!

ALL THAT RUNNING AWAY AND STUFF SAID, IF ANYONE HAS IDEAS ABOUT *HOW* TO ESCAPE I'M ALL FOR IT. JUST SHOUT 'EM OUT...NO BAD IDEAS.

EAT SHARK?

GRRRRR.

OKAY, *ONE* BAD IDEA, THERE WAS ONE BAD IDEA, BUT NOW BUN-BUN SAID IT, AND SO WE CAN MOVE ON.

THIS WOULD BE SO MUCH EASIER IF I EVEN KNEW WHAT ANY OF YOU CAN DO--

OOOH. YOU KNOW WHAT?!

I JUST BOUGHT THE EXPANSION PACK FOR THE "MONSTERS OF THE MARVEL UNIVERSE" CARD SET!

I KNEW THESE VERY SPECIFIC POUCHES FOR CARRYING TRADING CARDS WOULD COME IN HANDY *EVENTUALLY!*

...THANK YOU.

NO PROBLEM.

WE HAVE TO GET OUT OF HERE. WE'RE SITTING DUCKS.

SWSH

CHOMP

GOOD BOY.

HONOR GUARD, KRAVEN IS FOCUSED ON DEADPOOL...PROTECT YOUR KING AT ALL COSTS!

CMOSH

PROTECT THE KING!

HEY. DON'T DO THIS! I DON'T WANT ANYONE DYING ON MY ACCOUNT. I APPRECIATE THE GESTURE... MORE THAN YOU KNOW. BUT I'M HARD TO KILL. THIS JUST ISN'T NECESSARY!

DON'T FLATTER YOURSELF.

WHAT HAPPENS TO *MY* PEOPLE IF KRAVEN THE HUNTER KILLS *YOU* AND BECOMES THE NEW MONSTER KING?

YEAH. FAIR POINT. STILL.

I GET THAT I'M REALLY HILARIOUS AND SO YOU GUYS MAY NOT REALIZE IT...IT'S ADMITTEDLY SOMETIMES UNDERSOLD IN MODERN TIMES...

...BUT I'M A DEADLY ASSASSIN... I MEAN, I LITERALLY FIGHT...*FOR. A. LIVING.*

AREN'T YOU BROKE?

RIGHT, SURE. BUT THAT WAS JUST SOME BAD INVESTMENTS ON MY PART, NOT AN INDICTMENT OF MY SKILLS.

SERIOUSLY, YOU HAVE NO IDEA HOW FAST THE AVENGERS CAN BURN THROUGH A SAVINGS ACCOUNT.

HEY, NOW WE'RE TALKING! LOOK AT THIS! KOHLAAB THE PILE... THE GUY THAT'S MADE UP OF A BUNCH OF SMALL MAN BABIES CRUSHING ME RIGHT NOW?

HE'S GOT A PORTAL AT THE CENTER OF HIM! THAT'S OUR WAY OUT! SAYS IT WILL CLOSE AFTER THE LAST OF HIM GOES THROUGH IT HIMSELF!

KOHLAAB... IS THIS TRUE?

UH. YES?

KOHLAAB HATES THIS. GOING THROUGH A MONSTER'S PORTAL IS SO *PERSONAL*.

INDEED.

WELL, NO TIME FOR NICETIES! EVERYONE IN, HURRY!

HIGHNESS, IT'S YOUR TURN.

TAKE JEFF. I'LL FOLLOW WITH THE LAST KOHLAAB.

SIRE...

FWIP
FWIP
FWIP
FWIP
FWIP

THIS IS NOT UP FOR DEBATE! IT'S AN ORDER. WHY DO I KEEP HAVING TO TELL YOU THESE ARE ORDERS?!

YOU ARE RIGHT BEHIND US. YOU SWEAR?

TOTALLY.

ALSO? NEVER TRUST SOMEONE WHO SAYS TOTALLY.

KICK

NOOOOOO.

THIP

ALL RIGHT, KRAVEN...

...ENOUGH OF THIS COWARDLY THROWING CRAP AT ME FROM THE SAFETY OF... *SOMEWHERE ELSE.* THE "CANNON FODDER" ARE GONE. COME OUT HERE AND FIGHT ME MAN-TO-MAN.

...ISN'T THAT HOW IT SHOULD BE ANYWAY?

STAB

KRAK

THUNK

SHUNK

GRRKK!

?!

GURGLE...

THUNK

KRACK

ALL THIS RIDICULOUS LEAPING. LOOKS GOOD, BUT NOT AS EFFECTIVE AS YOU THINK IT IS.

HRRRRK.

SHIV

SKEWER

DOUBLE SKEWER

HNNNG.

UNGH.

SLUUUIICE

⊱KOFF⊰

AH! OUCH. SO MUCH OUCH. ⊱KOFF⊰ OH ⊱KOFF⊰ THANK THE VENGEFUL MONSTER GODS YOU DIDN'T CUT TOO DEEP AND I CAN TALK AGAIN! WHAT A LIVING NIGHTMARE THAT WAS!

IT WAS MERE MINUTES.

EXACTLY! I HAD SUCH A GOOD BURN WHEN I SKEWERED YOU AFTER YOU SAID MY LEAPING WAS RIDICULOUS AND NOW IT'S LOST FOREVER!

A TRUE TRAGEDY!

ARRRGGHHH!

SLING

A COWARD'S TRICK.

I THINK YOU MEAN TO SAY, SAVVY STRATEGY OF A GUY WHO'S FOUGHT NEARLY EVERYONE ON EARTH AND LIVED, BUT TO-MAY-TO, TO-MAH-TO!

FASH

FASH

THAP

THAP

THAP

YEAH, YOU'RE NOT THE ONLY ONE WHO CAN HIDE IN THE SHADOWS AND THROW THINGS AT PEOPLE.

YOU CALL SNOW A WEAPON?

TECHNICALLY NO, I JUST CALLED IT A "THING" BUT ALSO, NECESSITY, MOTHER OF INVENTION, BLAH, BLAH, BLAH.

"SNOW" IS NOT AN "INVENTION," DEADPOOL.

HEY. THAT'S KING DEADPOOL, LOSER.

ALSO...

STAB STAB STABBITY STAB STAB

EXTRA DEEP STAB

WAIT... DID THAT KICK DISLODGE MY DAMN EYEBALL? NO, NO, I'M GOOD.

MY EYE IS COOL, LET'S KEEP GOI--

YOU ASKED HOW I LIKE YOU?

SLICE

I LIKE YOU QUITE A BIT WITH ONE ARM.

DAMMIT!

Y'KNOW, I'VE NEVER BEEN A FAN OF THE EXCESSIVE CELEBRATION PENALTY... BUT I SEE THE ERROR OF MY WAYS NOW! WOE IS ME!

THIS IS HOW IT SHOULD BE, WILSON. BLOOD IS REAL. BLOOD IS TRUTH.

BAM

YOU SHOULD TEST OUT SOME OF THIS DIALOGUE, KRAVEN...'CUZ THAT CAME OUT REEEEEEEAL CREEPY.

AHA! I HAVE THE HIGH GROUND AGAIN! NOW THE SHOE'S ON THE OTHER...OH, I DON'T KNOW...SOMETHING SOMETHING ABOUT OUR SITUATIONS BEING REVERSED!

YOU KNOW, I KNEW YOUR DAD.

NOT THAT GREAT.

KRICK

DO YOU EVER TIRE OF THIS CLOWN YOU PLAY AT, WILSON?

I MEAN... WHAT YOU CALL THE "CLOWN" IS REALLY THE ONLY PART OF ANY OF THIS THAT'S FUN... WHY WOULD I TIRE OF *THAT*?

I SUPPOSE I THOUGHT YOU WOULD TIRE OF BEING THOUGHT A FOOL...BUT PERHAPS THAT IS ALL THERE IS. THE FOOL. CERTAINLY A REAL KING WOULD GIVE MORE OF A CARE FOR HIS PEOPLE.

THOSE WEREN'T *JUST* MY PEOPLE YOU KILLED, KRAVEN. BELLUS...THAT... HE WAS A FRIEND.

HARD TO TELL FROM YOUR BEHAVIOR. YOU ALWAYS ACT THE FOOL, NO MATTER THE CIRCUMSTANCES. EVEN WHILE MISSING AN ARM.

MISSING AN ARM? WELL, MUST BE A DAY THAT ENDS IN "Y"!

YOU LIVE THE LIFE I LIVE AND YOU LEARN TO TAKE YOUR PLEASURE WHERE YOU CAN FIND IT.

LIKE MAKING FUN OF YOU. CALL IT A SURVIVAL MECHANISM, CALL IT OLD HABITS, CALL IT A TIGHT FIVE AT THE LOCAL COMEDY SHOW.

SMACK

ALTHOUGH, IF YOU WANT THE TRUTH...TODAY YOU CAN CALL IT...

...A TRAP.

SO... I AM TO FIGHT YOUR UNDERLINGS THEN?

SO BE IT. I FEAR NO MAN OR MONSTER.

MRRRR!!!

ARRRGGHHH!

CRUNCH

FzZzzZTTT

HOW ABOUT A LITTLE BIT OF BOTH?

IT MAKES NO DIFFERENCE TO KRAVEN THE HUNTER.

OH GREAT. WE'VE ENTERED THE REFERRING TO HIMSELF IN THIRD PERSON PART OF THE BATTLE.

MRRRRR.

YOU ARE GOING TO GET YOUR SIDESHOW FREAKS KILLED, WOLF. ALL FOR A KING SUCH AS DEADPOOL?

...YES.

GRAAAH.

ZZZAAART

AH, THE GIANT RABBIT. HOW KIND OF YOU TO HAVE ONE VERY OBVIOUS TARGET...

...TO THROW SHARP OBJECTS AT.

?!

THUNK

LET US STAY CLOSE, MONSTERS...

MAKES YOUR SOFT BITS ALL THE EASIER TO SLICE TO RIBBONS.

HOW ABOUT YOU TRY THAT WITH KOHLAAB?

THINK YOU'LL FIND KOHLAAB HAS MANY MORE BITS...NONE OF THEM SOFT.

KOHLAAB! KOHLAAB! KOHLAAB! KOHLAAB!

KOHLAAB! KOHLAAB! KOHLAAB!

CLASSIC SUPER HERO LEAP!

LESS HEROIC KICK IN YOUR OPEN WOUNDS!

ARRRGGHHH!

YOU HAD ENOUGH YET? WHY DON'T YOU JUST MAKE IT EASY ON EVERYONE AND STAY THE EFF DOWN?

YOU *ARE* A COWARD. AFRAID TO FIGHT ME YOURSELF.

NAH. I'M JUST SMART ENOUGH TO KNOW IF YOU'VE GOT AN ARMY, *USE IT.*

HEH. YOUR *ARMY* CAN BARELY STAND.

WHO SAID I'M TALKING ABOUT *THIS* ARMY?

?!

ᐯ ⊃ Ϲ / ⊋ ᐯ ⅃ᗷ
ᗰ ○ ⤬

YES. *HIM* YOU CAN EAT.

TWO DAYS LATER.

...FOR DUST THOU ART, AND UNTO DUST SHALT THOU RETURN.

FARE THEE WELL, GOOD BROTHERS.

I'M SORRY, KID.

I NEVER SHOULD HAVE LET YOU GET WRAPPED UP IN ALL OF THIS.

PEOPLE STANDING NEXT TO ME GET DEAD. IT HAPPENS OVER AND OVER AGAIN.

I WAS DUMB TO THINK THAT YOU BEING A "MONSTER" WOULD MAKE YOU MORE IMMUNE TO THAT DEAD STUFF THAN THE USUAL FOLKS.

WRONG AGAIN, WADE.

OKAY, WE'RE GONNA GO HOME, BUDDY. I HOPE YOU LIKE CRAPPY BASEMENT APARTMENTS THAT SMELL LIKE FEET.

SO YOU'RE JUST GIVING UP, THEN?

CRASHING FUNERALS? REAL RESPECTFUL.

THE FUNERAL'S OVER, DARLING.

CAN YOU PLEASE FINALLY LEAVE ME ALONE NOW THAT I'M ABDICATING?

YOU SHOULDN'T SODDING ABANDON THEM JUST BECAUSE THINGS WENT PEAR-SHAPED, WADE. ✖✖✖✖✖.

WENT PEAR-SHAPED? ELEVEN MONSTERS DIED ON MY WATCH, ELSA...AND MY WATCH IS EXTREMELY #$*@& YOUNG. IT'S LIKE...STILL IN UTERO YOUNG.

DON'T BE A FOOL. YOU KNOW BETTER THAN MOST WHAT A VIOLENT WORLD THIS IS...

...EVEN MORE SO IF YOU'RE WALKING AROUND IN IT NOT BEING AND LOOKING HOW THE DODGY MAJORITY WANT YOU TO BE AND LOOK.

HORRIBLE THINGS HAPPEN. AS A LEADER IT'S YOUR JOB TO CARRY THAT WEIGHT AND DO BLOODY BETTER FOR THEM NEXT TIME.

MAYBE YOU SHOULD DO IT.

NO SODDING WAY. THERE'S NOT ENOUGH *ANYTHING* IN THE WORLD.

SO YOU DON'T WANT IT, BUT I SHOULD?

DON'T MAKE IT A BIG THING, WADE. I JUST MEANT YOU SHOULDN'T QUIT LIKE A WHINY SODDING BABY.

I SUPPOSE I'D ALSO SAY THAT NOBODY THINKS YOU CAN DO IT, AND IT'S A BLOODY GREAT WAY TO ✗✗✗ WITH THE LOT OF THEM.

...

NOW THAT *IS* TRUE.

STILL, I HATE HER.

AVENGERS MOUNTAIN. HOME OF THE AVENGERS.

AFTER THE BREAK WE'LL HAVE THE 1957 EPIC THE BRIDGE ON THE RIVER KWAI.

OH, TERRIFIC.

PROGRESSIVE INITIATIVES, LIKE THESE FART MONSTERS, MAKE OUR NEW ISLAND A PERFECT PLACE TO LIVE, WORK, AND PLAY!

I THINK IT IS GREAT.

IF STEVE ROGERS, CAPTAIN FREAKING AMERICA, AND, TRULY, AMERICA'S ASS, SAYS IT'S GREAT, WHO ARE YOU TO DISAGREE?! C'MON BY!

WADE!!!

ALASKA? MAYBE?

SHRRRRRKKKK.

SMASH

SPLORRRRRR

YES, ÷KOFF÷ YOU HAD BETTER RUN.

YOU WANTED AN ENEMY, LITTLE KING? WELL, AN ENEMY YOU SHALL HAVE.

I SHALL NOT REST UNTIL I HAVE KILLED DEADPOOL, THE UNKILLABLE MAN.

WADE & JEFF!

YOU KNOW I HAVE PLANS, RIGHT, JEFF?

MRRR!

LIKE, I'M AN ACTUAL *KING* NOW, KID. I GOT RESPONSIBILITIES COMIN' OUT MY EARS...

...AND OTHER LESS PLEASANT PLACES.

MRRRRP!

WHAT I'M SAYING IS THAT THERE BETTER BE A GOOD POINT TO THIS LITTLE EXCURSION, JEFFREY.

IF AT THE END OF THIS THERE'S JUST SOME GROSS, DEAD GARBAGE FISH YOU FOUND, OR LIKE THAT ONE TIME WITH THAT MONSTER THAT SORTA ALMOST LOOKED LIKE A GIANT SENTIENT SHRIMP, I'MMA BE REAL ANNOYED.

MRRRR!

OH.

OH NO. NO WAY. UH-UH.

MRRRRRRR!

ONLY FOR *YOU* DO I DO THIS, JEFFREY.

THIS IS NICE. I MEAN, SURE, IT'S NOT THE MAGNIFICENT ORGIES AND SWIMMING IN POOLS OF GOLD THAT I'VE BEEN HOPING FOR, BUT SITTING QUIETLY ON A BENCH WATCHING JEFFREY PLAY IS A HUGE UPGRADE.

YOU SHOULDN'T LET THEM PLAY.

OH. NOT YOU AGAIN. IS THERE NO PEACE FOR ME?!

I DON'T USUALLY SAY THIS TO INSANELY HOT WOMEN BUT MY GOD, WOMAN, CAN YOU PLEASE LEAVE ME ALONE?!

I'M A MONSTER HUNTER, WADE. SO LONG AS YOU'RE KING OF THE BLOODY MONSTERS, I'M AFRAID OUR FATES ARE RATHER INTERTWINED.

A MONTH AGO I WOULD'VE BEEN PUMPED ABOUT SOME SEXY "FATES BEING INTERTWINED" TROPE.

BUT NO. IT'S THIS. CAREFUL WHAT YOU WISH FOR, KIDS!

I'M NOT BLOODY JOKING, WADE.

I KNOW. IT'S THE MOST IRRITATING THING ABOUT YOU. WAIT, NO, THAT'S WHEN YOU "TRY TO HURT ME FOR MY OWN GOOD," BUT YOU NOT BEING FUNNY IS DEFINITELY THE SECOND MOST IRRITATING THING.

I...I REALLY THOUGHT I GOT THROUGH TO HIM THERE FOR A MINUTE.

I THOUGHT YOU DID TOO.

YOU WERE RIGHT, THOUGH. NOW HE'S DEAD ANYWAY AND SO ARE TWO INNOCENT BUT STUPID HUMANS THAT SHOULDN'T HAVE BEEN OUT HERE.

I'M NOT SURE I *WAS* RIGHT.

I...MONSTERS ARE MY WHOLE SODDING LIFE, AND HAVE BEEN SINCE BEFORE *I* CAN REMEMBER.

IT'S EASY TO ASSUME THEY'RE ALL THE BLOODY SAME, TO TREAT *THEM* ALL THE SAME...BUT THAT'S A MISTAKE.

MAYBE I'VE FORGOTTEN THAT A LITTLE BIT. IT WAS GOOD TO BE REMINDED.

THANK YOU.

BUT THE CIVILIANS.

WE LIVE IN A VIOLENT WORLD. THERE ARE ALWAYS CASUALTIES, WADE.

--AND THE X-MEN HAVE BEEN **SO** SNOOTY ABOUT THEIR FANCY KRAKOA GATES, WHICH IS TOTALLY NUTS BECAUSE EVEN THOUGH I'M NOT A MUTANT, IF YOU CONSIDER THE FACT THAT THANKS TO MY MOVIES MOST PEOPLE IN THE WORLD BELIEVE **I AM** A MUTANT...AND WE ALL KNOW THAT IF ENOUGH PEOPLE BELIEVE IT THEN IT'S BASICALLY TRUE. AND SO **I SHOULD** TOTALLY BE ABLE TO GET INTO KRAKOA ON LIKE...A **TECHNICALITY.** BUT DO THEY EVEN ANSWER PHONE CALLS ABOUT THIS? THE ANSWER IS NO. **NO, THEY DON'T.** MEANWHILE THEY'RE IN THERE SITTING ON MAYBE THE CURE FOR CANCER, AND IT'S LIKE, **HELLO, I HAVE THE CANCER, MAN.** LIKE, HOW MANY TIMES DO I HAVE TO HELP THOSE JACKASSES BEFORE THEY GIVE A CRAP ABOUT ME? I MEAN, YES, ROGUE CALLED ME BACK, I'LL GIVE HER THAT, BUT WHEN I CALLED **HER** BACK I HEARD SHE WAS A TREE NOW...BUT THEN SOMEONE ELSE SAID SHE WAS A LIGHTHOUSE.* IT WAS ALL VERY CONFUSING. WHICH, ADMITTEDLY, IS VERY ON-BRAND FOR THE X-MEN. BUT STILL!

*SOUND INSANE? IT IS! IN A GOOD WAY! READ EXCALIBUR, TRUE BELIEVERS!--ED.

SO...WHAT YOU'RE SAYING IS THE X-MEN ARE xxxxxxxx JERKS?

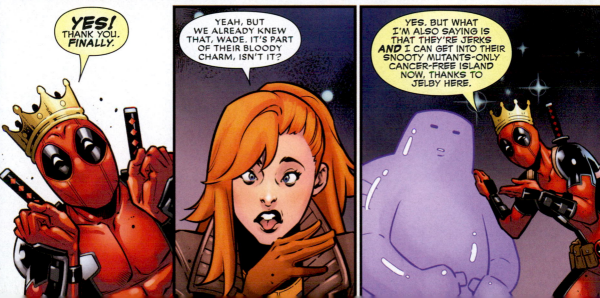

YES! THANK YOU. **FINALLY.**

YEAH, BUT WE ALREADY KNEW THAT, WADE. IT'S PART OF THEIR BLOODY CHARM, ISN'T IT?

YES. BUT WHAT I'M ALSO SAYING IS THAT THEY'RE JERKS **AND** I CAN GET INTO THEIR SNOOTY MUTANTS-ONLY CANCER-FREE ISLAND NOW, THANKS TO JELBY HERE.

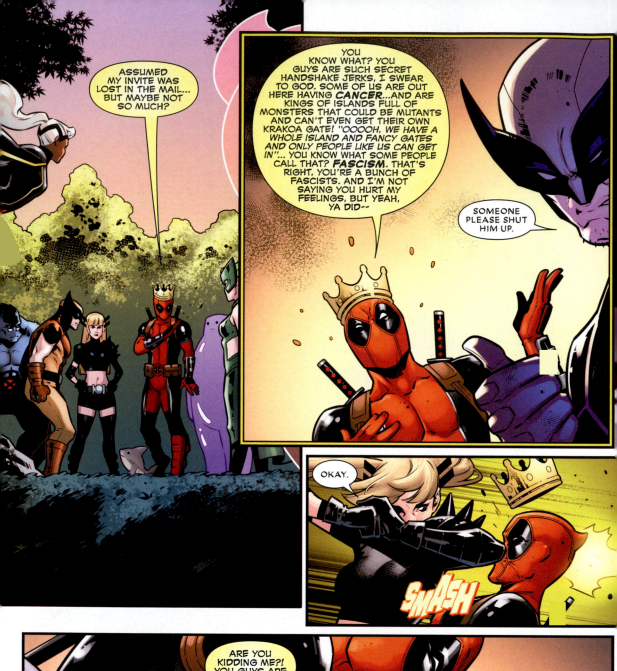

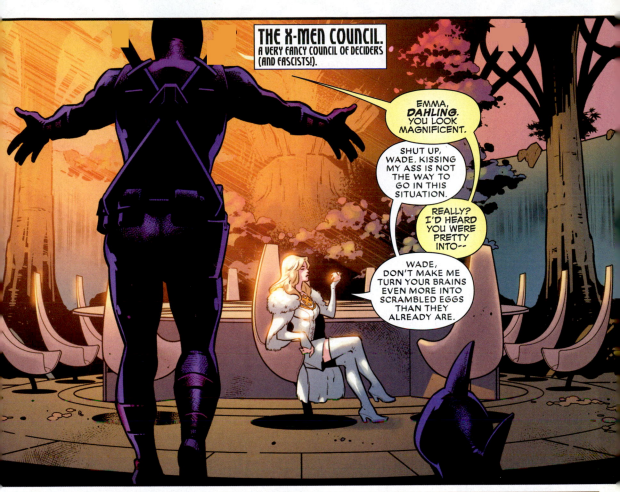

THE X-MEN COUNCIL.
A VERY FANCY COUNCIL OF DECIDERS (AND FASCISTS!).

EMMA, *DAHLING*, YOU LOOK MAGNIFICENT.

SHUT UP, WADE. KISSING MY ASS IS NOT THE WAY TO GO IN THIS SITUATION.

REALLY? I'D HEARD YOU WERE PRETTY INTO--

WADE, DON'T MAKE ME TURN YOUR BRAINS EVEN MORE INTO SCRAMBLED EGGS THAN THEY ALREADY ARE.

ALSO, WHAT IS THAT THING BESIDE YOU? IT LOOKS LIKE A FABULOUS HANDBAG WITH LEGS AND TEETH. I MUST HAVE IT.

GASP! HOW *DARE!* IT'S NOT A THING--OR A HANDBAG--IT'S A *JEFF*. JEFFREY THE FIRST OF HIS NAME OF THE FORMER STATEN ISLAND, TO BE EXACT.

HMMM. I STILL SAY IT'S A DANGEROUS HANDBAG. BUT I LOVE IT.

WELL, YOU *CAN'T* HAVE HIM.

VERY WELL. BACK TO BUSINESS. ROGUE HAS MADE AN IMPASSIONED PLEA ON YOUR BEHALF, NOTING THAT YOU SHOULD HAVE BEEN INVITED TO VISIT GIVEN BOTH YOUR NEW STATUS AS KING OF STATEN ISLAND AND ALSO AS SOMEONE WHO HAS FREQUENTLY BEEN A FRIEND AND ALLY. NOW--

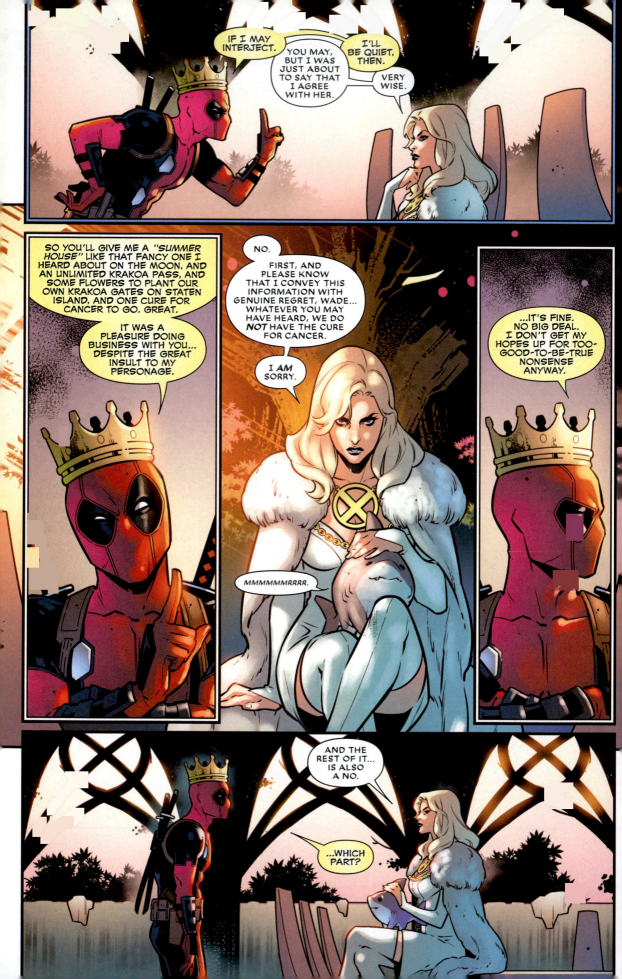

FIVE MINUTES LATER,
IN THE KRAKOAN FLOWER FIELDS.

I'M TAKING THIS FLOWER WITH ME AND YOU CAN'T STOP ME!

ARRRRGGHHHH!

DAMMIT, WADE. DON'T MAKE IT LIKE THIS!

YOU GUYS MADE IT LIKE THIS FIRST BY BEING...

HA!

FLIP

TOO SLO-- ARGGGH!

KRACK

THE ISLAND FORMERLY KNOWN AS STATEN.

WE DON'T NEED THEIR PITY. WE DON'T NEED **ANYONE'S** PITY. WE'RE KINGS. WELL, ME, **I AM**. YOU, NOT SO MUCH.

THE X-MEN WANT FANCY LAWS? **I'LL** SHOW 'EM FANCY LAWS!

ALTHOUGH I **DO** APPRECIATE THAT THEY ONLY MADE THREE LAWS AND ONE OF THEM IS ABOUT GETTING BUSY. YOU KNOW, WE ALL TAKE THE **X** IN X-MEN FOR GRANTED, BUT REALLY WE SHOULDN'T DO THAT ANYMORE. I THINK WE KNOW THE TRUTH NOW.

AND I CAN'T BELIEVE JELBY STAYED THERE WITH THEM! I'M SURROUNDED BY TRAITORS.

MRRRRR?

BANG BANG

MRRRR.

BARF

AW. A KRAKOA FLOWER COVERED IN SHARK BARF.

APOLOGY ACCEPTED, BUD. ALTHOUGH, IF I'M HONEST, I FORGAVE YOU THE SECOND YOU BIT LORNA ON HER LEG.

MRRR!

ANYWAY, WHO CARES WHAT THE MUTANTS DO NOW THAT THE FIRST NEW RULE OF NU-STATEN ISLAND IS...

...THEY'RE NOT ALLOWED ON *MY* ISLAND.

NO MORE MUTANTS

NICE SIGN. DID YOU HAVE SOME BLOODY PRIMARY SCHOOLERS MAKE THAT FOR YOU?

LISTEN. SOMETIMES YOU'RE NICE TO ME AND SOMETIMES YOU'RE MEAN, AND WHILE YOU'RE ALWAYS HOT, WHICH ALMOST MAKES EVEN THE MEAN TIMES WORTH IT, I'M GONNA BE REAL WITH YOU...I'VE HAD A ROUGH DAMN DAY AND I'M REAL EMOTIONALLY TAPPED RIGHT NOW AND I CAN'T TAKE IT.

SO CAN WE JUST TABLE THE CONFUSING SEXUAL TENSION FOR LATER?

SORRY, WADE. I'M AFRAID WHAT I'VE GOT GOING ON IS MORE URGENT THAN SEXUAL TENSION.

DON'T BE ABSURD. NOTHING'S MORE URGENT THAN GOOD SEXUAL TENSION.

WADE, NO MORE BLOODY JOKES...

...I'M ✕✕✕✕✕✕✕ DYING.

NEXT: TRUE LOVE STORY!

#1 VARIANT BY
CARLOS GÓMEZ
& JASON KEITH

#1 VARIANT BY
DAVID FINCH
& GURU-eFX

#2 VARIANT BY
IRKA ANDOLFO
ARIF PRIANTO

#3 MARVELS X VARIANT BY
DAVID YARDIN
& MORRY HOLLOWELL

#4 GWEN STACY VARIANT BY
MIKE HAWTHORNE
& DAVE McCAIG

#4 VARIANT BY
PHILIP TAN
& JAY DAVID RAMOS

#5 SPIDER-WOMAN VARIANT BY
MIRKA ANDOLFO

#6 MARVEL ZOMBIES VAR
KHOI PHAM
& MORRY HOLLO